1 Samuel 17

God Had A Plan

For David

Created by Cindy Kirkland
Book Design by Julie Bryant

Printed in the United States of America

ISBN 13:   9798841259572

Story written by Cindy Kirkland

godhadaplanbooks@gmail.com

Book Design & Layout by Julie Bryant

juliebryant20@sbcglobal.net

Bible quotations are taken from and inspired by the International Children's Bible, New Century Version, Copyright 1986, 1988 by Word Publishing.

Some free clipart for commercial use and public domain from:
Microsoft Publisher 2010   www.wpclipart.com
www.gospelgifs.com   www.openclipart.org
www.clipartlord.com

Some purchased clipart with commercial use and credit from:
Mygrafico.com   Graphics by Mygrafico
Pretty Grafik at Mygrafico   Mels Brushes at Mygrafico
Sanqunetti Design at Mygrafico

Napa, California

2022

God Has a Plan for YOU!

 Jeremiah 29:11-13

"I know the plans I have for you," says the Lord, "for you to have the best in all you do... I plan to look ahead and bless you. So trust Me. Pray to Me and call Me and I will hear you. And when you look for Me with all your heart you will find Me."

Hello, my name is David. I love to sing and pray to God all the time. I am happy every day because I get to go out to a big grassy field and take care of our sheep. Every one of our little lambs has a name. What is your name?

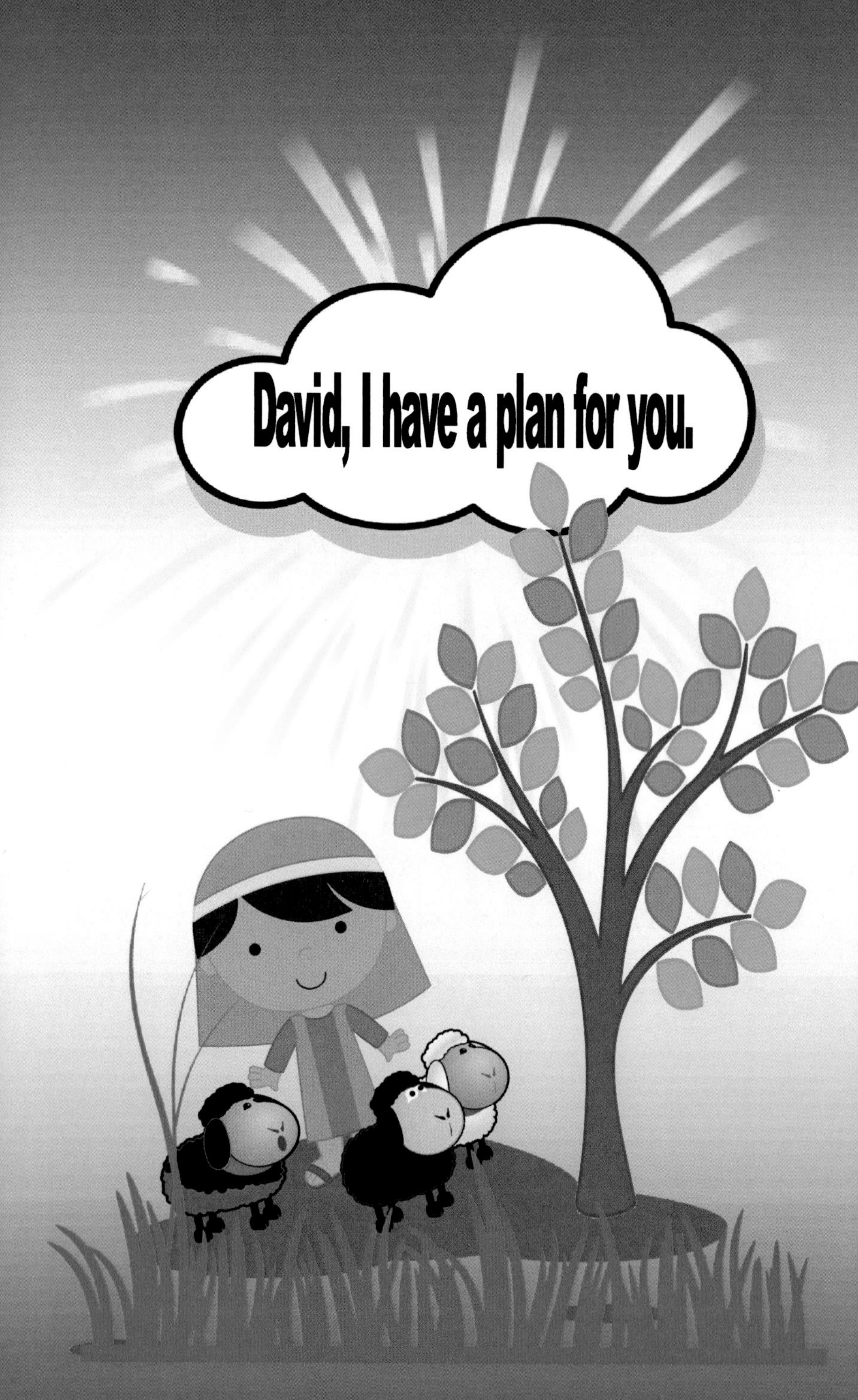
David, I have a plan for you.

Sometimes I feel like a little lamb too. God calls my name and I look up and I talk with Him. He helps me take care of all our sheep. Sheep need a lot of care. So do we. Sometimes bad things can happen to them.

One day when I was taking a nap on the grassy field I heard a loud roar! What was it? It was a big lion. The lion was going to hurt my sheep! Was I afraid? NO! I prayed to God. I grabbed the lion by the neck and he fell down dead.

"GROWL..." What was that? I looked up and saw a big brown bear coming to kill my sheep. Was I afraid? NO! I prayed to God. I grabbed the bear by the neck and he fell down dead. I killed a lion and a bear!

I have another job too. My dad asked me to take some food to my big brothers. They work in the army of Israel. When I got to the army camp all the men in the army were yelling, "HELP! HELP! There is a big bad giant named Goliath yelling at us. He wants to kill us."

Was I afraid? NO! My God of the armies of heaven will fight for me. Just as he helped me kill the lion and the bear, he will help me kill this big giant too! My brothers were not nice to me. They kept saying I was too small.

The king of Israel told me to come see him. When I got there he gave me a big helmet, a big shield, a big sword, and some big boots. I put them on. No way! These are too big for me. I cannot wear all this stuff. The king said I was small too.

I took the army weapons off and went to get a sling. I also went to pick up 5 smooth stones. When Goliath the giant came out to see me he laughed at me. He said I was too small. Was I afraid? NO! I told him that the armies of heaven were going to kill him.

Goliath laughed and laughed, "Ha! Ha! Ha!" I took a stone and put it in my sling. It went around and around. It flew across the sky. The stone hit the big bad giant in the head. BAM! He fell down dead.

The king and all the army men yelled, "Hooray! Goliath is dead! Goliath is dead! Little David was right. The God of heaven's armies came to help him kill the big bad giant." God will always help you and I when we need him the most. Now the whole world will know how big and powerful God is.

I want to tell you about a time when a man of God came to my house to see my dad. He told my dad to go get all my brothers. He was going to pick one of them to be the King of Israel some day.

All my brothers came to see the man of God. The man looked at each one of them. He said, "Not this one. Not this one. Not this one." He looked at all 7 sons. He asked my dad if he had any more sons. My dad said, "Yes. My little son named David is not here. He is taking care of our sheep."

The man of God said, "Go get him." The man of God told my dad that I was the one God wanted to be the King of Israel. God had a big plan for me. He has a big plan for you too!
I know God will help me be a great king one day.

My heart is so big for God.
I love to pray and sing to
Him all the time. I love to
write down my songs and
prayers. You can read
them in the Bible. They are
called the Psalms. (soms)

Here are a few verses from some of the Psalms.

Psalm 8

Lord, God, your name is the most wonderful name in all the earth. You make babies and children sing to you. I look up in the sky and see the moon and all the stars you made. I can see all the sheep, the cows, the wild animals, and the birds in the sky. I can see the fish in the sea and every creature that lives under the water. You made them all.

Psalm 9

God, I will praise you with all my heart. I will tell of all your miracles you have done. I will be happy because of you. I will sing praises to your name.

Psalm 24

The earth and everything in it belong to the Lord. The world and all its people belong to the Lord.

Psalm 25

My God, I trust you. Lord, tell me your ways. Show me how to live. I will trust you all day long.

Psalm 27

Wait for the Lord's help. Be strong and brave and wait for the Lord's help.

Psalm 29

The Lord's voice is powerful. The Lord's voice is majestic. With your help God, I can attack an army. With your help I can jump over a wall.

Psalm 33

The Lord looks down from heaven. He sees every person. He watches everyone who lives on the earth.

Psalm 34

Happy is the person who trusts the Lord. Children, come and listen to me. I will teach you to worship me.

Psalm 37

Trust the Lord and do good. Enjoy serving the Lord and he will give you what you want. Trust him and he will take care of you.

Psalm 47

Clap your hands, all you people. Shout to God with joy. Sing praises to God. God sits on his holy throne.

Psalm 145

Parents will tell their children about all the amazing things you do. I will tell how great you are. He does not get mad but is full of love. The Lord keeps his promises. All living things look for food. You give it to them at the right time. The Lord is close to everyone who prays to him.

Psalm 148

Praise the Lord from the heavens. Praise him high above the earth. Praise him all you angels. Praise him all you armies of heaven. Praise him sun, and moon and shining stars. Praise him all you sea animals. Praise him all you oceans. Praise him lightening and hail, snow and clouds. Praise him stormy winds. Praise him mountains and all hills and fruit trees . Praise him wild animals and all cows, crawling animals and birds. Praise him kings of the earth and all nations. Praise him young men and women, old people and children.

Psalm 149-150

Sing a new song to the Lord. Praise him with dancing. Praise him with tambourines, harps and stringed instruments and flutes. Praise God in his Temple. Praise him for his strength. Praise him for his greatness. Praise him with trumpet blasts. Praise him with loud drums and cymbals. Let everything that breathes praise the Lord.
PRAISE THE LORD!

Made in the USA
Middletown, DE
31 July 2022